C000019451

Across the Curriculum: SCIENCE for ages 8-9

A wide range of teachers' notes and photocopiable worksheets to address the needs of teachers and children in covering several aspects of the curriculum, while learning valuable concepts in science.

Across the Curriculum: Science for ages 8–9

Contents

Across the Curriculum: Science for ages 8–9

Contents

We show possible curriculum links but we will not have thought of everything so you may like to add some of your own.

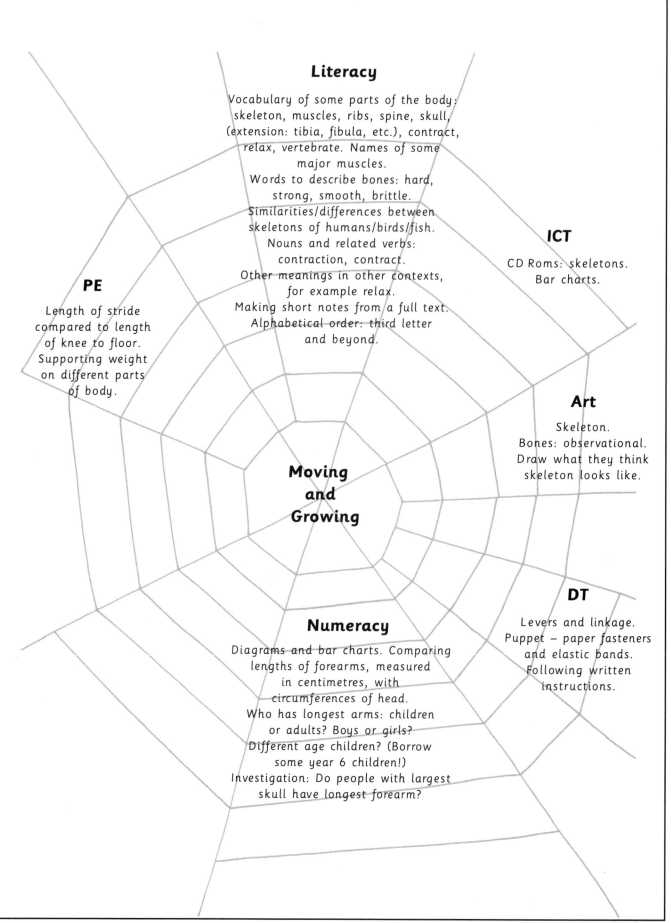

Literacy

Vocabulary of some parts of the body: skeleton, muscles, ribs, spine, skull, (extension: tibia, fibula, etc.), contract, relax, vertebrate. Names of some major muscles.
Words to describe bones: hard, strong, smooth, brittle.
Similarities/differences between skeletons of humans/birds/fish.
Nouns and related verbs: contraction, contract.
Other meanings in other contexts, for example relax.
Making short notes from a full text.
Alphabetical order: third letter and beyond.

ICT

CD Roms: skeletons.
Bar charts.

PE

Length of stride compared to length of knee to floor. Supporting weight on different parts of body.

Art

Skeleton.
Bones: observational.
Draw what they think skeleton looks like.

Moving and Growing

DT

Levers and linkage.
Puppet – paper fasteners and elastic bands.
Following written instructions.

Numeracy

Diagrams and bar charts. Comparing lengths of forearms, measured in centimetres, with circumferences of head.
Who has longest arms: children or adults? Boys or girls?
Different age children? (Borrow some year 6 children!)
Investigation: Do people with largest skull have longest forearm?

Andrew Brodie Publications © A & C Black Publishers Ltd.

Worksheet 1 is a vocabulary sheet that can be used to form an initial assessment of children's prior knowledge. There are actually twelve pairs of ribs but it is very unlikely that the children will be able to feel them all; the bottom two pairs of ribs are known as 'false ribs' and are attached at the back. Accordingly, our picture of the skeleton only shows ten pairs of ribs. In looking at the bones of the arms and legs we would expect the children to notice that there are two lower bones and one upper bone on each limb.

Worksheet 2 provides further information about human bones, together with a literacy exercise on alphabetical order. This exercise gives children the opportunity to learn the spellings of some technical vocabulary concerning the body.

Worksheet 3 continues the theme of 'bones'. Children are asked to write a summary of the passage using forty words or less. Summarising text is a very difficult task and children may need to make several attempts; however, it is extremely worthwhile for children to be able to summarise effectively.

Worksheet 4 contains detailed technical information regarding muscles, tendons and ligaments. The children should read this information carefully, perhaps with adult help, then hand back the sheet and attempt to complete Worksheet 5. You may like to give Worksheet 4 back to them if they are struggling with Worksheet 5, then take it away again while they continue.

Worksheets 6, 7 and 8 are all centred around an investigation into whether people with the largest skulls have the longest forearms. On Worksheet 6 children are asked to measure the forearms of six friends, then to plot the results on to a bar chart and colour all the bars blue. Worksheet 7 asks the children to measure around the heads of their six friends, then to plot these results but this time to arrange them in order of size and to colour them red. Finally, Worksheet 8 asks them to plot both sets of results together: the children should plot the red results first, then the blue results. Children can be encouraged to consider how to show both sets of data on one bar chart. They could colour one set on top of the other:

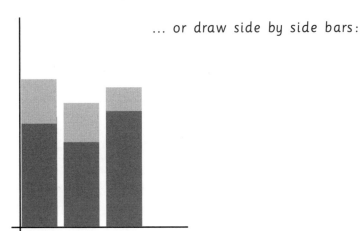

... or draw side by side bars:

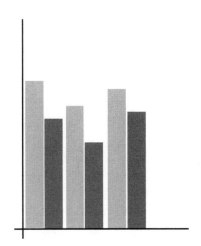

Worksheet 8 should provide opportunities for discussion, enabling children to answer the question, 'Do people with the largest skulls have the longest forearms?' They may well find that there is no match between the two sets of data, but could then consider what data may be more likely to provide a match: for example, length of forearm compared to length of leg from knee to floor.

Name: Date:

The skeleton

Label the skeleton using the words below:

ribs

eye socket

spine

skull

upper arm

forearm

kneecap

fingers

toes

pelvis

Try to feel your own ribs.
How many do you think you have? ☐

How many can you see on the skeleton? ☐

Look at the skeleton's legs. How many long bones are there? ☐

Describe the positions of these bones.

_____

_____

Look at the skeleton's arms. How many long bones are there? ☐

Describe the positions of these bones.

_____

_____

What does the word 'socket' mean?

_____

Name:

Date:

Body vocabulary

The **spine** consists of lots of **bones**. Each **bone** is called a **vertebra**. The plural is **vertebrae**.

The **skull** is at the top of the spine. The **pelvis** is connected to the lower part of the spine.

The **ribs** are also connected to the spine.

Try to feel your own spine. Can you feel all the vertebrae?

The bone at the very bottom is the **coccyx**.

The spine

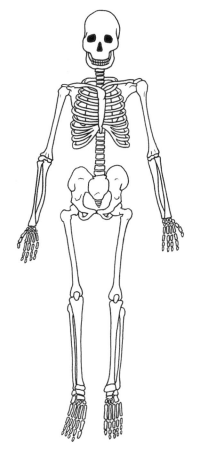

The skeleton

Rewrite the underlined words, putting them in alphabetical order.

Remember:

● The word 'bone' will come before the word 'bones'.

● If the first letters of the words are the same, look at the second letters.

● If the second letters are the same, look at the third letters.

1 _____   2 _____

3 _____   4 _____

5 _____   6 _____

7 _____   8 _____

9 _____

Name: | Date:

Bones

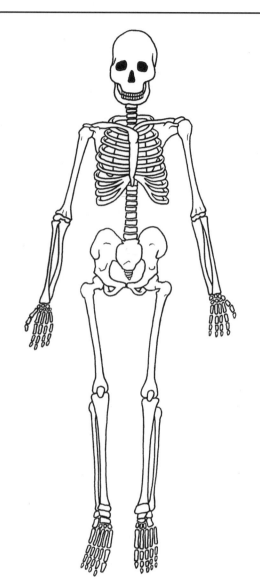

Our skeleton forms the framework for our whole body. The skeleton consists of a large number of bones.

Some bones are big, some are very small. They are quite hard and they have a whitish colour. All of our bones are very important, but the ribs have a special job because they protect the heart and lungs.

Some bones are solid, but most of them are hollow. The hollow areas contain marrow. Our blood cells are made in the bone marrow.

How many words are there in the passage of writing about bones?

Try to find the most important points from the passage.
Write a summary of the passage using only forty words or less.
You may need to try this a couple of times as it is not easy.

_____

_____

_____

_____

_____

_____

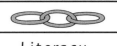
Name: Date:

Muscles

Muscles are strong fibres that are attached to our bones. They enable us to make movements. Every time we want to move, our brain sends a message to our muscles.

The muscles are joined to the bones by strong cords called tendons.

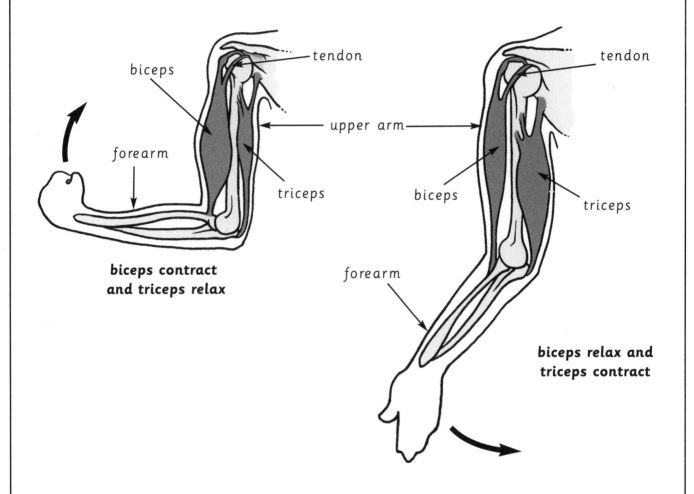

biceps · tendon · forearm · upper arm · triceps

**biceps contract
and triceps relax**

biceps · tendon · upper arm · triceps · forearm

**biceps relax and
triceps contract**

Look carefully at the diagrams of an arm. We have illustrated the bones of the upper arm and forearm, as well as the main muscles that move the forearm.

You can see that the biceps muscles and triceps muscles are attached to the top of the upper arm, at the shoulder. When we lift the forearm the biceps contract, they get shorter and fatter, and the triceps relax. When we lower the forearm the triceps contract and the biceps extend.

Name: | Date:

Muscles

Read Worksheet 4 and look carefully at the diagrams. When you think that you understand it, and can remember the main points, give it back to your teacher!

Try to complete this sheet without having to look back at Worksheet 4.

Use these words to label the diagram:

biceps   triceps   upper arm   forearm   tendon

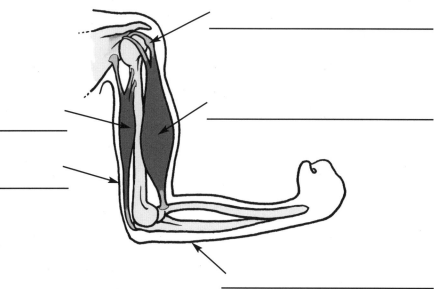

Why do we have muscles?

_____

_____

What joins our muscles to our bones? _____

What happens to our biceps when we raise our forearm?

_____

_____

What happens to our triceps when we raise our forearm?

_____

_____

Andrew Brodie Publications © A & C Black Publishers Ltd.

Name: Date:

Investigation sheet A

Do people with the largest skulls have the longest forearms?

You are going to measure the forearms of six friends.

Name of person	Length of forearm (cm)

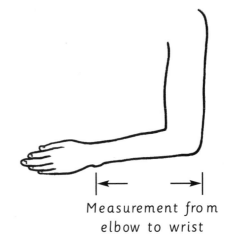

Measurement from elbow to wrist

Plot your results on a bar chart. Colour all the bars blue.

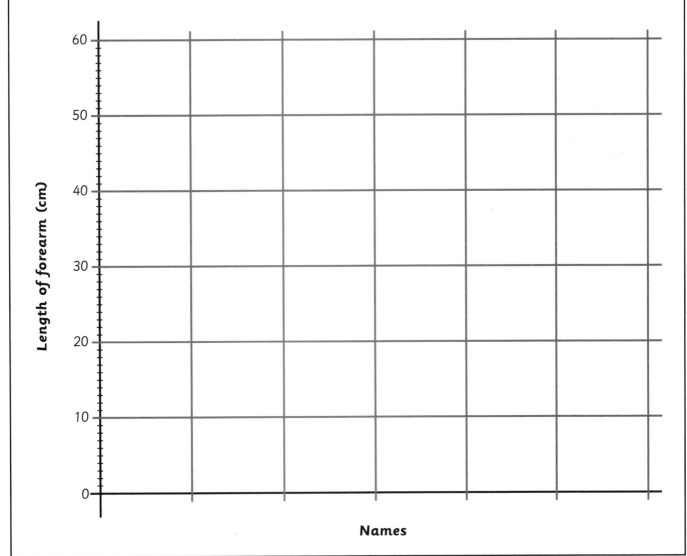

Length of forearm (cm)

Names

Name: | Date:

Investigation sheet B

Do people with the largest skulls have the longest forearms?

You are going to measure around the heads of the same six friends as you used for sheet A.

Name of person	Circumference of head (cm)

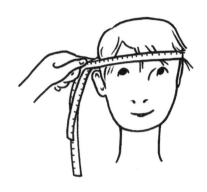

Plot your results on a bar chart, arranging them in order of size from smallest to largest. Colour all the bars red.

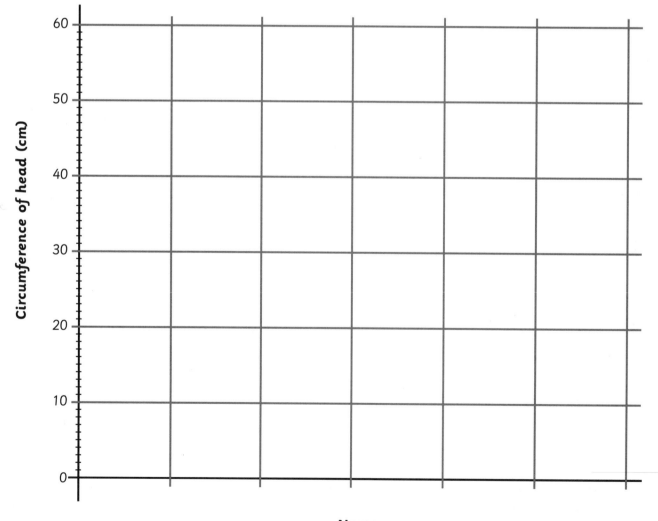

Names

Andrew Brodie Publications © A & C Black Publishers Ltd.

Name:

Date:

Investigation sheet C

Do people with the largest skulls have the longest forearms?

Look again at sheets A and B. Sheet B should show the circumference of your friends' heads. The bar chart on sheet B should show these results in order from smallest to largest. Copy these results on to the bar chart below, then add the correct data for the forearm of each person. Now colour the data for forearms blue and the data for heads red.

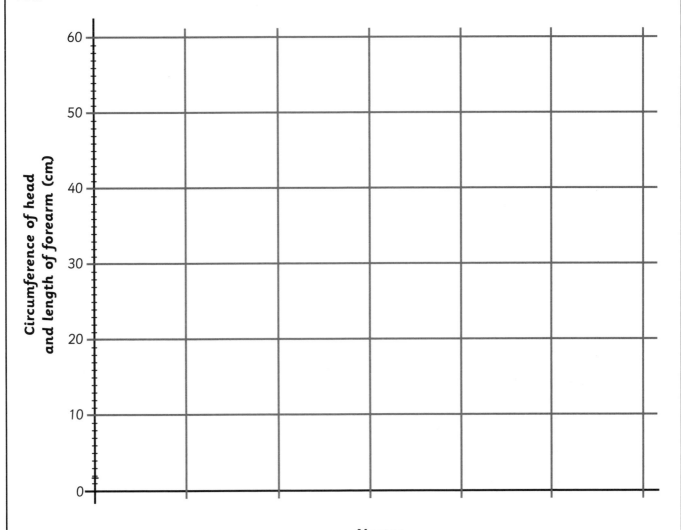

Names

Is there a pattern to your results?

_____

_____

Can you think of another investigation where you make comparisons?

_____

_____

We show possible curriculum links but we will not have thought of everything so you may like to add some of your own.

Literacy

Vocabulary: life processes, nutrition. Habitat: condition, organism, predator, prey, producer, consumer, food chain.
Organism as a term for all living things: sorting into plants/animals (include trees, worms, spiders, etc.).
Definition of habitat. Mini-habitat, micro-habitat.
Adjectives to describe habitats: cool, damp, dark, etc. Could consider particular creatures and where they could be found, then use adjectives to describe these places.

ICT

Collecting information on data handling programme.

Art

Observational drawing of invertebrates, for example woodlice, worms, snails, centipedes, etc., or of flowers such as dandelion.

Habitats

Geography

Tour school and find different habitats: ponds, field, wood, tree, hedge, flower bed, lawn, plant trough, under leaf, under stone.
Plan of school and where different habitats are found.

Numeracy

Need to be able to measure temperature, time, distance.
Classifying and sorting pictures of animals/plants – how are children choosing to sort them? (Pictures of bee, wasp, spider, beetle, dandelion, daisy, etc.)
Eight compass positions: north, south, east, west, north-east, north-west, south-east, south-west.

Andrew Brodie Publications © A & C Black Publishers Ltd.

Worksheet 1 provides appropriate scientific vocabulary and introduces a simple system of classification of organisms. Children should be encouraged to realise that the plant and animal kingdoms each include a huge variety of organisms. Some children may need support when considering the classification process: some will not appreciate that an oak tree is a plant as is grass; the animal kingdom includes humans but also greenfly. For many years fungi were classified as part of the plant kingdom but it is now recognised that they should be classified separately. Again, children will need help in identifying the mushroom, toadstool and yeast as fungi.

Worksheet 2 introduces correct terminology for food chains. The children will need to be aware that the food chain always starts at the bottom of the diagram i.e. with a green plant. This is known as the 'producer'. Children will be able to relate to the titles of the consumers as 'primary' and 'secondary' as these titles are obviously similar to school titles; 'tertiary' will probably be new to them.

Worksheets 3 and 4 are used together. The answers are:

Evergreen trees: pine, holly	Not evergreen trees: oak, beech
Yellow flowers: buttercup, dandelion	Not yellow flowers: grass, nettle
Eight legs: spider	Insects: greenfly, ant
Birds: robin, sparrowhawk	Not birds: worm, snail, mouse

Worksheet 5 requires children to show eight points of the compass in the correct position. They can make use of this sheet when working on Worksheet 6.

Worksheets 6 and 7 ask children to visit the school grounds, identifying different mini-habitats and discovering organisms there. You may wish to prepare some mini-habitats for them, for example by placing stones or old logs in damp areas. The results could be used to form a class display and could then provide opportunities for discussion regarding types of habitat and whether particular areas of the school have particular species.

Worksheet 8 encourages children to measure and observe carefully. This should help with accuracy in both art and numeracy.

Name: Date:

Organisms

All living things are called organisms.

Organisms can be sorted under three headings: **plants**, **animals** and **fungi**.

Read the names of the organisms below, then write them under the correct heading.

oak	**sparrow**	**buttercup**	**yeast**
snail	**spider**	**mushroom**	**whale**
grass	**greenfly**	**toadstool**	**seaweed**
daisy	**woodlouse**	**salmon**	**pine**
	grasshopper	**ant**	

plants

animals

fungi

Andrew Brodie Publications © A & C Black Publishers Ltd.

Name: **Date:**

Food chains

The animal that eats the primary consumer is known as the **secondary consumer**.

foxes eat rabbits

The animal that eats the producer is known as the **primary consumer**.

rabbits eat grass

The green plant is known as the **producer**.

We describe the fox as a **predator** and the rabbit as **prey**.
It is easier to understand the diagram above by starting at the bottom.
Read about the producer first.

Here is another food chain.

sparrowhawk

What is the producer?

_____

robin

What are the consumers?

_____ _____ _____
primary   secondary   tertiary

caterpillar

The sparrowhawk preys on the robin. We call the

sparrowhawk a _____.

We call the robin its _____.

rose leaves

Name: | Date:

Classifying organisms – sheet A

Use this sheet with Worksheet 4.

oak tree

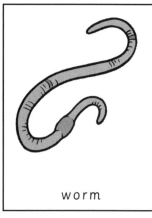

worm

spider

mouse

dandelion

pine tree

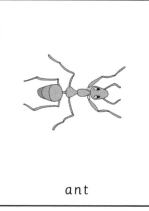

ant

robin

holly tree

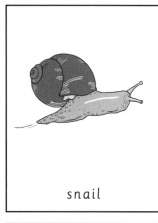

snail

beech tree

grass

greenfly

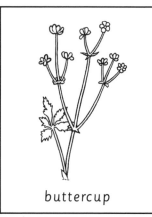

buttercup

sparrowhawk

nettle

Andrew Brodie Publications © A & C Black Publishers Ltd.

Name: Date:

Classifying organisms – sheet B

Look carefully at the organisms on Worksheet 3.
Working on only one organism at a time, follow the questions below to find the correct place to write the name of the organism.

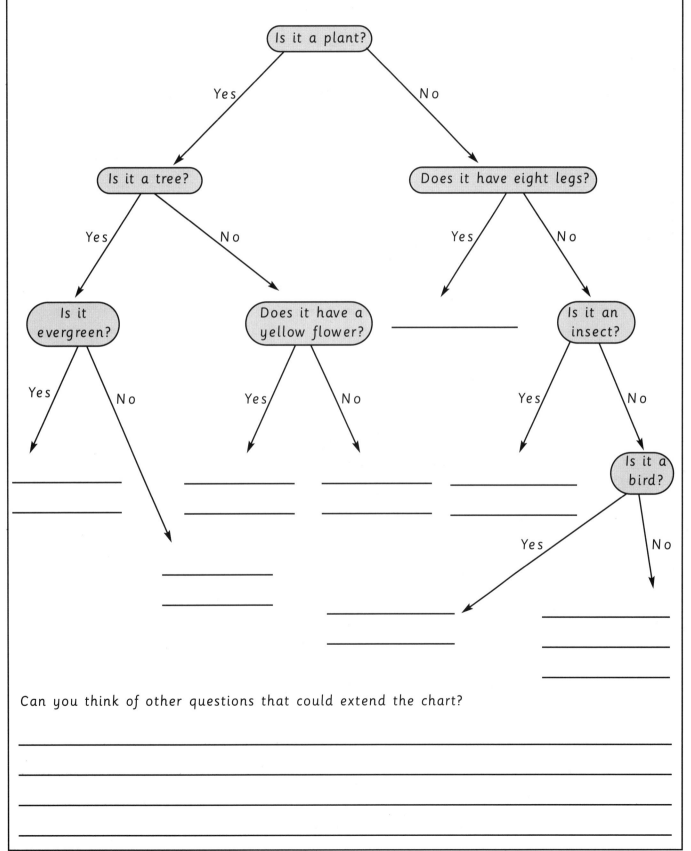

Can you think of other questions that could extend the chart?

_____

_____

_____

_____

Name: Date:

Points of the compass

Most maps and plans are drawn to show north at the top.
Use this sheet as your personal reminder of the points of the compass.
Write the words in the correct places on the sheet.

north   **south**   **east**   **west**

north-east   **north-west**   **south-east**   **south-west**

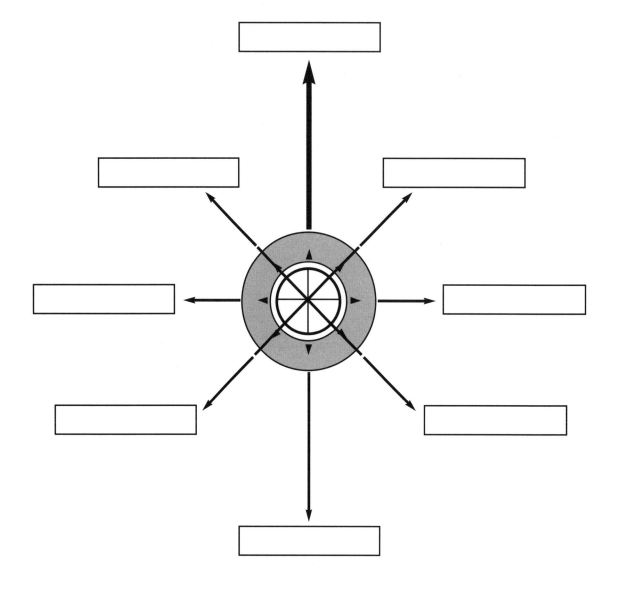

Name:

Date:

Mini-habitats

As a class, choose someone to draw a large plan of the school to go on the wall. Remember that north should be at the top.
Working in small groups, the rest of the class should visit different mini-habitats to gather information. Each group should record information from just one of the mini-habitats. This information can be added to the plan, with suitable illustrations.
Record the information for your habitat here.

N
W   E
S

Name of mini-habitat: _____

Position in school (north, south, etc.): _____

Size of habitat being observed: _____

Ground surface (concrete, grass, soil, etc.): _____

Conditions of habitat (damp, dry, etc.): _____

Organisms found at the habitat:

Plants	Animals	Fungi
....	....	....
....	....	....
....	....	....
....	....	....
....	....	....

Sketches of organisms found:

Name: | Date:

Different habitats

The school is a **habitat** for lots of different organisms.
Different parts of your school form **mini-habitats**. For example,
a pond, a hedge or a tree could all be described as
mini-habitats.
In the mini-habitats you will find **micro-habitats**. For example,
a leaf, a plant pot or under a stone could all be described as
micro-habitats.

Find some mini-habitats and micro-habitats in the school.
Write the names of these habitats in the chart. Draw ticks in the
boxes under the words that describe the habitat you have found.
We have provided an example for you.

Habitat	dry	wet	damp	shady	sunny	dark	light
under a stone			✓	✓		✓	

Andrew Brodie Publications © A & C Black Publishers Ltd.

Name:

Date:

Flowers

This is a scale drawing of a daisy. We have not drawn it to actual size.

Look carefully at the picture.
How many leaves can you see?

Count the petals on one flower
How many are there?

Your job is to find a dandelion, or another plant with a flower, then draw it very carefully. You should use a ruler to measure the diameter of the flower, the length of the stem, the lengths of the leaves, the width of the leaves and the length of the petals.
Count the number of leaves and the number of petals.
Draw the plant here.

We show possible curriculum links but we will not have thought of everything so you may like to add some of your own.

Literacy

Words and phrases regarding warmth and cold: temperature, thermometer, degrees Celsius, thermal, conductor, insulator. Related nouns and verbs: conductor, conduct, insulator, insulate, room temperature. Words in different contexts, for example conductor (bus, music), degrees.

ICT

Collect, store and retrieve temperatures. Word processing and font sizes, for example for posters.

PE

Why we don't wear much in PE.

Art

Poster: keeping things warm and cold. Wrapping, etc.

Keeping Warm

Geography

Plan or map of classroom showing which areas are hot and which are cold. Guess temperatures and record actual temperatures over 24-hour period. (Could use a maximum/minimum thermometer.)

DT

How to keep something cold, trying different wrappings for example bubble wrap, card, newspaper, etc.

Numeracy

Temperature. Length in standard measures (including mm). Construct table of results, for example of warming or cooling.

Worksheet 1 is a vocabulary sheet covering words that relate to temperature. Children are encouraged to use dictionaries to find definitions and to realise that some words may have more than one definition. At the foot of the page the children are asked to arrange words in alphabetical order. For some children, the process of looking beyond the first letter will be new. Looking at 'thermal' and 'thermometer' will help them to understand this process. Note also that the children will need an explanation that 'warm' is written before 'warmer'.

Worksheet 2 is a practice sheet for reading temperatures on thermometers. You will find it helpful to complete this sheet with the children before giving them a real thermometer to work with.

Worksheets 3 and 4 deal with temperature differences within the classroom. Most children will need some help in drawing the plan of the classroom: it need only be a sketch plan but they should attempt to position it appropriately relative to north. In discussion, they will probably identify sunshine and windows as two possible influences on the temperatures.

Worksheet 5 is a practice sheet for reading measurements on a ruler accurately. By providing adult support at this stage, years of inaccuracy can be prevented!

Worksheet 6 presents an investigation into keeping water warm. Small plastic water bottles are ideal for this activity. If possible, fill several bottles at the same time using warm water from a tap rather than from a kettle. Tap water in school should be at a safe temperature but it is essential that you check it for safety. You may choose to allocate specific materials to each group to avoid several groups choosing the same material to use as an insulator. Children should be discouraged from seeing this as a competition between themselves but rather a competition between the materials.

Worksheet 7 has a similar investigation but this time the children are attempting to keep something cold. Encourage them to speculate as to whether the material that was most successful in the previous activity will be most successful here.

Worksheet 8 concerns insulating homes. You could ask the children to research their own homes. They must ask their parents for help in identifying insulation within the home and should not attempt to look in the loft by themselves. They are likely to find out that water tanks are insulated as well as, perhaps, the windows, walls and loft.

Name: Date:

Temperature vocaulary

If we look up the word **conductor** in a dictionary, we find that there is more than one definition.
Find the definition of conductor that is relevant to the topic of keeping warm. Copy the definition here.

_____

_____

_____

Is the word **conductor** a noun or a verb?   _____

Is the word **conduct** a noun or a verb?   _____

Find the definition of **insulator** and write it here.

_____

_____

Here are some more words that we may use in our work on 'keeping warm'.

temperature	degrees	thermometer	
Celsius	thermal	insulate	warm
cold hot	cool	warmer	cooler

Rewrite the words in alphabetical order.

_____   _____   _____

_____   _____   _____

_____   _____   _____

Name: | Date:

Degress Celsius

We need to be able to read temperature in degrees **Celsius**.
What temperatures are shown on these thermometers?

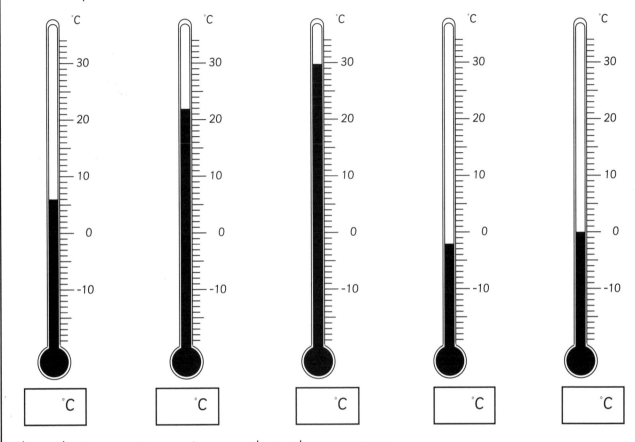

| °C | °C | °C | °C | °C |

Show the temperatures given on these thermometers.

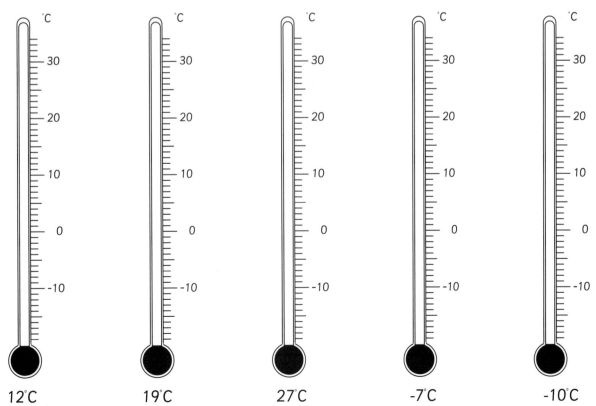

12°C   19°C   27°C   -7°C   -10°C

Andrew Brodie Publications © A & C Black Publishers Ltd.   27

KEEPING WARM

Name: Date:

Classroom temperatures

Draw a simple plan of your classroom. Remember that north should be at the top of the plan. Mark areas on your plan, using these points of the compass: **N, S, E, W, NE, NW, SE, SW.**

For example, your classroom plan could look like this:

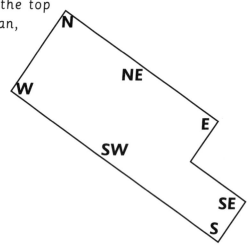

Which part of the classroom do you think is the coolest? _____

Make an estimate of the temperature there.   ☐

Which part of the classroom do you think is the warmest? _____

Make an estimate of the temperature there.   ☐

Andrew Brodie Publications © A & C Black Publishers Ltd.

Name: Date:

Classroom temperatures

Put a thermometer in four areas of the classroom, including the area you think is warmest and the area you think is coolest.

Record the temperature every hour throughout the day.

°C

Time	Area 1	Area 2	Area 3	Area 4

Are all the temperatures the same? _____

Describe the results, saying which areas are warmer and which are cooler.

_____

_____

_____

Did the sun shine on any of the areas? _____

_____

Can you explain your findings? _____

_____

_____

_____

Name:

Date:

Accurate measurements

Sometimes we need to measure things accurately, for example we might want to measure an ice cube. We could measure its width, depth and height. (If it's a proper cube, these will all be the same measurement.)

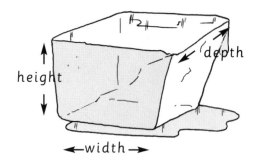

For accurate measurement we can use millimetres.

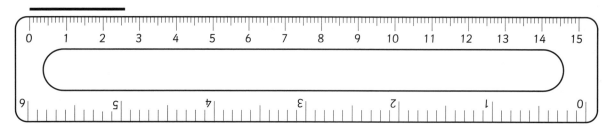

You can see that the black line is 2 centimetres and 6 millimetres long. As there are 10 millimetres in every centimetre, we can say that the line measures 26 millimetres.

2cm 6mm = 26mm

Measure the lines below, recording your results in millimetres.

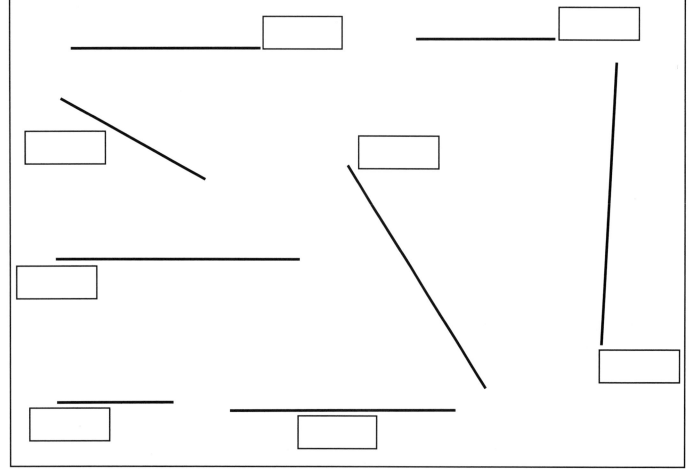

Andrew Brodie Publications © A & C Black Publishers Ltd.

Name: **Date:**

Keeping warm: an investigation

You will need: A small bottle and a variety of materials
to choose from.

**small
bottle**

newspaper

fabric

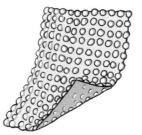

bubble wrap

**polystyrene
chips**

You are going to fill a bottle with warm water. Your task will be to keep the water
warm for as long as possible, using one of the materials as an insulator.
Choose **one** of the materials to wrap your bottle in.
Which one have you chosen and why?

_____

_____

_____

Which of the materials do you
think will be the poorest insulator? _____

Prepare your materials before you wrap the bottle.
Record the temperature of the water at the start, then every ten minutes.

Time									
Temperature									

Compare your results with other people's.
Which insulation worked most effectively?_____

Name: Date:

Keeping cool: an investigation

You will need: An ice cube and a variety of materials to choose from.

ice cube

newspaper   **fabric**   **bubble wrap**   **polystyrene chips**

You are going to choose one material to act as an insulator. When you are ready to start, wrap the ice cube in your chosen insulator. Every ten minutes you should unwrap the ice cube to see how much it has melted. Make sure you wrap it up well again after looking at it.

Time	Description of ice cube

Compare your results with other people's.
Which insulator worked most effectively? _____

Name: Date:

Insulating our homes

We use different heat sources to warm our homes. Can you name some?

_____   _____   _____

We try to keep the house warm by insulating it.

How do we insulate:

the windows? _____

_____

_____

the walls? _____

_____

_____

the roof? _____

_____

_____

the floors? _____

_____

_____

We show possible curriculum links but we will not have thought of everything so you may like to add some of your own.

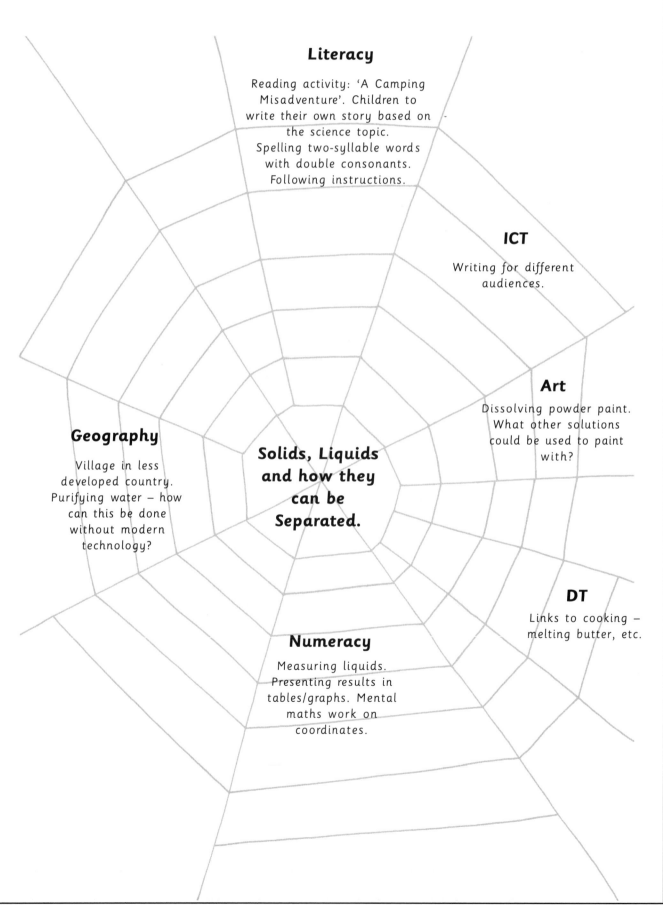

Literacy

Reading activity: 'A Camping Misadventure'. Children to write their own story based on the science topic. Spelling two-syllable words with double consonants. Following instructions.

ICT

Writing for different audiences.

Art

Dissolving powder paint. What other solutions could be used to paint with?

Geography

Village in less developed country. Purifying water – how can this be done without modern technology?

Solids, Liquids and how they can be Separated.

DT

Links to cooking – melting butter, etc.

Numeracy

Measuring liquids. Presenting results in tables/graphs. Mental maths work on coordinates.

Worksheet 1 contains an activity that is ideal for paired work. This could be done at the beginning of the science topic to assess children's understanding. After further experience of this topic, the children could complete the follow-up activity on Worksheet 7.

Worksheet 2 contains vocabulary related to familiar solids and liquids. When they have completed the wordsearch the children should be able to create the message, 'Liquids take the shape of the container they are poured into.' This message could provide opportunities for some discussion and this would be well supported by demonstrating pouring a liquid into different containers so that children can observe the fact that liquids do take the shape of their containers.

Worksheet 3 involves a crossword of two-syllable words with double consonants. You may wish to discuss some of the relevant words with the children before giving them this worksheet.

  Answers across: 2 butter, 3 blotting, 5 swimming, 8 dissolve.
  Answers down: 1 funnel, 4 getting, 5 settling, 6 coffee, 7 pepper.

Worksheet 4 provides an ideal numeracy starter to link with the science topic. The answers to the puzzles are: LIQUID, MELT, SCIENCE, FREEZE, THAW, INVESTIGATION.

Worksheet 5 is similar to Worksheet 4 but considerably more difficult! This sheet should be used as an extension activity for more able children who are able to deal with coordinates in four quadrants. The answers to the puzzles are: DISSOLVE, MIX, SOLUTION, WATER, FILTER, SEPARATE, POWDER.

Worksheet 6 provides opportunities for pupils to practise reading the scales on various measuring cylinders, to accurately measure liquids.

Worksheet 7 uses ICT to present a challenge, linked to 'A Camping Misadventure'. This is ideal at the end of the science topic when children should be familiar with items of equipment, processors and likely outcomes.

Worksheet 8 can be for use as homework. The final column is for discussion and group decision. Class or group results could be used to present data in graph forms.

Name: Date:

A Camping Misadventure

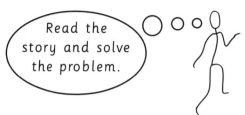

Read the story and solve the problem.

The Bure family were camping. Little Jack was standing at the table inside the tent playing with his cars. He used some storage tins as buildings for the cars to drive around.

One tin contained rice.
One tin contained flour.
One tin contained dried peas.

Jack was enjoying his game.
He took the lids from the tins to use as 'roundabouts'.
As he was playing, one of the tins tipped over and knocked both the others over too. On the table was a mixture of rice, flour and peas.

Dad saw what had happened.
"Oh no!" he said "We were going to cook the rice this evening. Whatever can we do?"

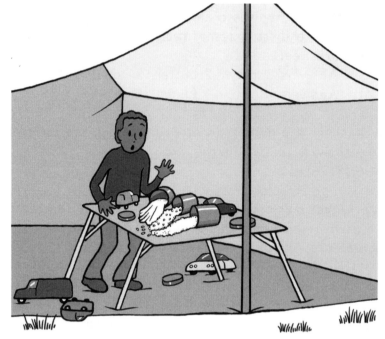

With a partner work out how the three items could be separated again.
Draw a diagram in the box below to show your idea and use the lines for a written explanation.

Name:

Date:

Solids and liquids

Follow the clues to find five familiar solids and five familiar liquids in the wordsearch.
Shade them on the wordsearch and then write them in the correct boxes.

- Material from a tree.

- This freezes to become ice.

- Iron, steel or copper perhaps.

- Send this at times of celebration.

- Wash your hair with this.

- The liquid from fruit.

- Used in windows.

- Drink for baby mammals.

- Many modern items are made from this.

- Vegetable, olive and sunflower are three types of this.

Solids

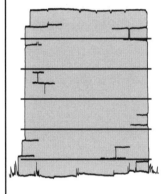

w	o	o	d	l	b	i	q	u	i	o	d	s	p
a	t	j	a	x	k	e	g	b	t	h	i	e	l
t	s	u	h	m	e	t	a	l	a	z	p	l	a
e	e	i	o	f	i	b	t	h	a	e	x	c	s
r	o	c	z	n	t	l	a	i	n	s	e	r	t
t	x	e	h	b	e	y	k	a	r	b	s	e	i
p	o	z	u	r	x	b	e	z	x	d	b	i	c
n	c	a	r	d	t	s	h	a	m	p	o	o	o

Liquids

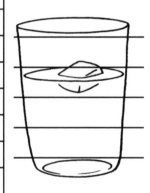

Now shade in all the letters b, x and z.
Reading from left to right, starting at the top, you should be able to read an interesting fact.

Write it below.

_ _ _ _ _ _   _ _ _ _   _ _ _   _ _ _ _ _ _ _   _ _   _ _ _

_ _ _ _ _ _ _ _ _   _ _ _ _   _ _ _ _ _ _ _   _ _ _ _ _.

Name: Date:

Words with double consonants

The words in the quiz below might be used in your work on liquids and solids.
They are all words with double consonants in them.
The first answer has been done for you.

Clues across

2. This melts quickly when warmed. Some people spread it on bread!

3. This paper soaks up liquids.

5. A way of moving through water.

8. Sugar or salt may do this in water.

Clues down

1. You might pour things through this.

4. When the temperature goes up, we say "It is _ _ _ _ _ _ warmer."

5. If you mix sand and water the sand slowly sinks to the bottom. We say it is _ _ _ _ _ _ _ _ .

6. Dissolve granules of this in hot water to make a drink.

7. Salt and _ _ _ _ _ _ are often used to add flavour to food.

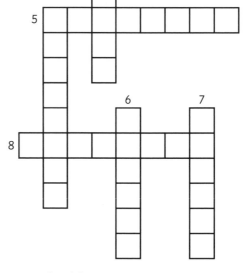

Use the spaces below to write twelve more 'double consonant' words. Make each word a **noun** that is either a solid or a liquid.
You may need a dictionary to help you.

_____   _____   _____   _____

_____   _____   _____   _____

_____   _____   _____   _____

Name:

Date:

Grid maths 1

See how quickly you can decode the words below.
Each pair of numbers will lead you to a letter marked on the grid.
The first word has been done for you.

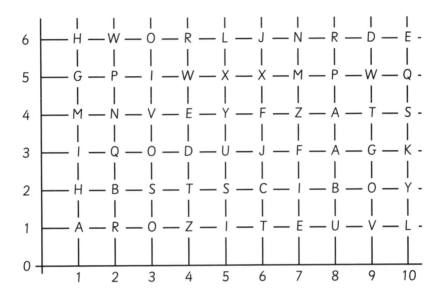

5,2   3,1   5,6   3,5   4,3

S   **O**   **L**   **I**   **D**

10,1   5,1   10,5   8,1   1,3   9,6

—   —   —   —   —   —

7,5   4,4   10,1   9,4

—   —   —   —

10,4   6,2   3,5   4,4   7,6   6,2   10,6

—   —   —   —   —   —   —

7,3   2,1   7,1   10,6   4,1   7,1

—   —   —   —   —   —

6,1   1,2   1,1   4,5

—   —   —   —

1,3   7,6   3,4   4,4   3,2   9,4   5,1   9,3   8,3   4,2   3,5   3,6   2,4

—   —   —   —   —   —   —   —   —   —   —   —   —

Now, see if
you can set some 'grid
point' words for a friend
to decode.

Name: | Date:

Grid maths 2

See how quickly you can decode the words below.
Each pair of numbers will lead you to a letter marked on the grid.
Watch out for the negative numbers!
The first word has been done for you.

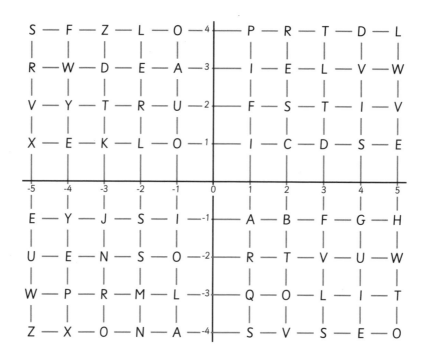

4,1   1,3   2,3   3,-2   -5,-1

S I E V E

-3,3 1,1 2,2 -2,-2 -1,-2 5,4 4,3 -4,1

— — — — — — — —

-2,-3 -1-1 -4,-4

— — —

-5,4 -1,4 3,-3 -1,2 3,2 4,2 2,-3 -3,-2

— — — — — — — —

-5,-3 -1,3 -3,2 -2,3 -3,-3

— — — — —

1,2 4,-3 3,3 5,-3 -4,-2 -2,2

— — — — — —

-2,-2 2,3 -4,-3 1,-1 2,4 -1,3 3,4 -2,3

— — — — — — — —

1,4 5,-4 -4,3 4,4 4,-4 2,4

— — — — — —

Andrew Brodie Publications © A & C Black Publishers Ltd.

Name: _____ Date: _____

Measuring liquids

Look at the containers of liquids and answer the questions about them.
All the measurements show how many millilitres of liquid (ml) there are.

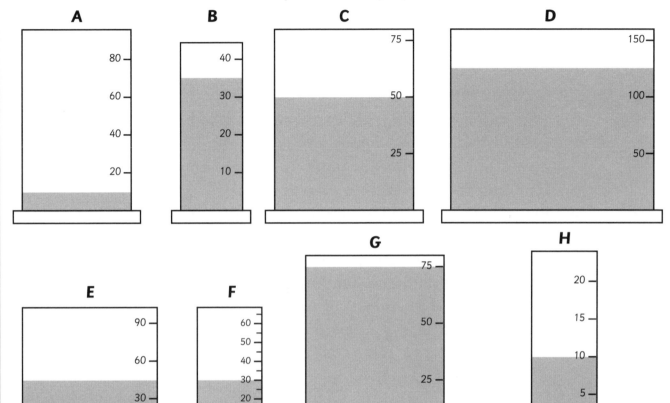

How much liquid is in each container?

A = _____ **B** = _____ **C** = _____ **D** = _____

E = _____ **F** = _____ **G** = _____ **H** = _____

Which container has most liquid in? _____

Which two containers have the same amount of liquid in? _____

Which container holds most liquid when filled? _____

Which container holds least liquid when filled? _____

Shade the containers below to show the liquid to the correct levels.

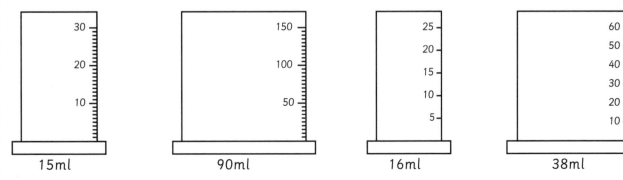

15ml   90ml   16ml   38ml

Name: Date:

Problems for your classmates

Do this activity with a partner.

1
- ☆ Did you enjoy doing the challenge 'A Camping Misadventure'?
- ☆ Using all you know about solids and liquids, make up your own story challenge for your classmates to do.
- ☆ Use only items available in school.
- ☆ Present your challenge clearly by writing it on the computer.
- ☆ Ensure the key points are presented very clearly.
- ☆ Think about what style and size of font you use.
- ☆ Use headings and sub-headings where needed.
- ☆ Ensure any instructions included are ordered correctly.
- ☆ Use the spellcheck – after, all there's no excuse for incorrect spellings with the computer to help you!

2
- ☆ Later your teacher will let you try each other's challenges.

3
- ☆ When you have done someone else's challenge discuss with them how good you think their presentation was. Could anything be improved?

Have fun!

Andrew Brodie Publications © A & C Black Publishers Ltd.

| Name: | Date: |

A kitchen cupboard investigation

Look in the larder cupboard and/or fridge at home. Can you see five liquid items and five solid items in there? Fill in the chart below using your ten items. Make your own title for the final column.

LIQUIDS

name of item	used in cooking?	for drinking?	used daily/weekly/ occasionally?	

SOLIDS

name of item	used in cooking?	eaten raw?	used daily/weekly/ occasionally?	

Andrew Brodie Publications © A & C Black Publishers Ltd.

We show possible curriculum links but we will not have thought of everything so you may like to add some of your own.

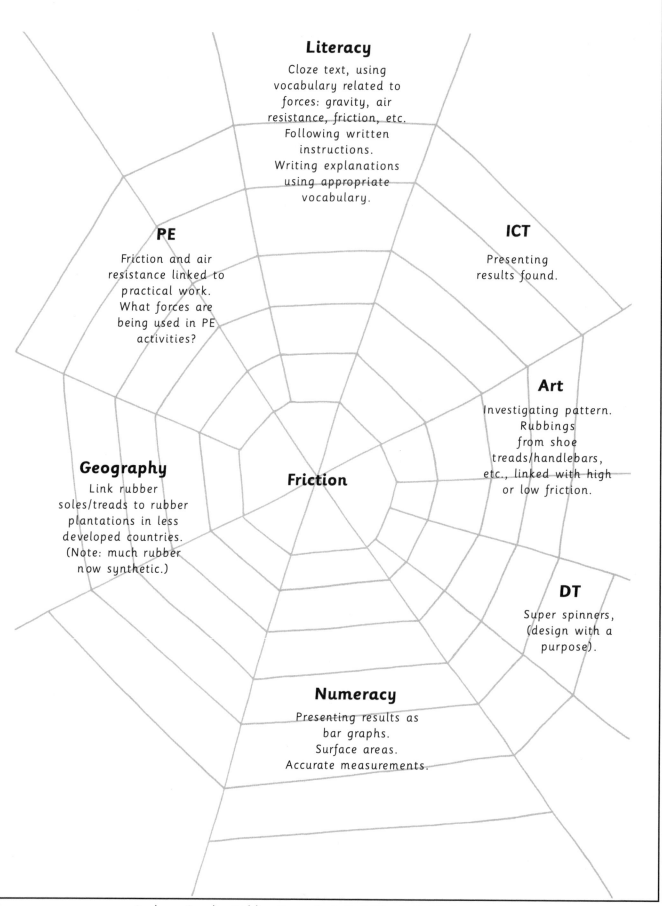

Literacy
Cloze text, using vocabulary related to forces: gravity, air resistance, friction, etc. Following written instructions. Writing explanations using appropriate vocabulary.

PE
Friction and air resistance linked to practical work. What forces are being used in PE activities?

ICT
Presenting results found.

Art
Investigating pattern. Rubbings from shoe treads/handlebars, etc., linked with high or low friction.

Geography
Link rubber soles/treads to rubber plantations in less developed countries. (Note: much rubber now synthetic.)

Friction

DT
Super spinners, (design with a purpose).

Numeracy
Presenting results as bar graphs. Surface areas. Accurate measurements.

Worksheet 1: cloze test to assess/reinforce children's understanding of forces. For ease of marking, the order of the answers is as follows: pulls; forces; gravity; surface; resistance; windy; friction; high; easily; low.

Worksheets 2, 3 and 4 cover aspects of literacy (following instructions), DT (designing for a purpose) and numeracy (accurate measurement – presenting results).

Worksheet 2 is suitable for OHP/group use. You will need to provide the children with a variety of papers and thin card, together with some paperclips and sticky tape. You may want the children to produce plans for their super spinners before making them. Alternatively, they could make the spinners and experiment with them before drawing the design of their most successful version. In either case, you may wish to make use of Worksheet 4 for this purpose.

Worksheet 3 introduces a mathematical element in the recording of results, as the 'winner' of each pair competes against the 'winner' of another pair until a 'champion' is reached. It is then, of course, ideal for the winner from each group to compete to find a class champion. Only one sheet per group is needed.

Worksheet 4 is DT based and provides prompts and frames for recording details of making the spinner and of the evaluation of the finished product. Children should be encouraged to measure their spinners accurately and to record the measurements on the design.

Worksheet 5 involves asking children to begin to relate shape to air resistance. The children could be asked whether the sheet presents a fair test and may realise that it is testing more than one thing at once: shape and area. Testing shape only, by keeping the area of each shape the same, would be a very difficult activity. As an extension activity you could ask the children to make a fair test of the effect of surface area on air resistance. The children could design one shape and repeat this shape in several different sizes: the easiest shape for this is probably a square.

Worksheet 6 covers the presentation of results on a bar chart. The children are asked to interpret the bar chart. It may be necessary to explain that once the shoes had slipped off they were not replaced, as they would have slipped at all subsequent angles and the bar chart would have shown cumulative figures. They should find the following answers:

$3, \frac{1}{10}$ (The answer $\frac{3}{30}$ is acceptable.)

$5, \frac{1}{6}$ (The answer $\frac{5}{30}$ is acceptable.)

More than half the class. ($\frac{17}{30}$)

Worksheet 7 has space for illustration and description of a test that children create to test for friction. They may choose to test shoe treads having already worked on the results presented on Worksheet 6.

Worksheet 8 links the theme of 'forces' to sporting activities. You may like to spend part of a PE lesson discussing the forces that childrens are using and experiencing in their activities.

Name: | Date:

Forces

Use words from the box to complete the text below.

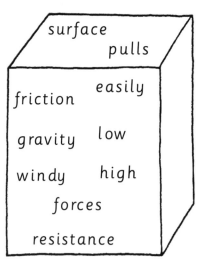

surface

pulls

friction   easily

gravity   low

windy   high

forces

resistance

- The pushes and _____ that we know as _____ are all around us every day.

- _____ is the force that pulls everything towards the earth's _____ .

- We are usually unaware of air _____ , but on a _____ day we can feel the air pushing against us.

- The resistance that happens when one surface pushes against another is called _____ .

- A strong friction that prevents things from moving easily is called _____ friction.

- When items slide _____ against one another there is _____ friction.

Andrew Brodie Publications © A & C Black Publishers Ltd.

Name:

Date:

Super spinner challenge 1

Your task is to make a spinner that takes as long as possible to reach the ground when dropped from a set height.

A basic design for your spinner is shown here.

1. Cut along dotted line. ⎯⎯⎯⎯⎯⎯⟶

2. Fold one wing forward and the other backwards at the grey line.

✔ You may make your spinner larger or smaller.

✔ You may choose what type of paper to use.

✔ You may wish to use paperclips or sticky tape to add weight to your spinner.

✔ You may alter the proportions of your spinner.

Before you make your spinner think about all the above points. Remember: you want your spinner to take as long as possible to reach the ground. You must think about how to make your spinner get the most benefit from the air resistance.

Have fun!

Name: Date:

Super spinner challenge 2

Your teacher will have helped you to sort out groups of eight children.
Each group must think of a fair test for the spinners.
Complete the chart below as each pair of spinners is tested against each other. The winner of each test then competes against another winner until a champion super spinner is found.

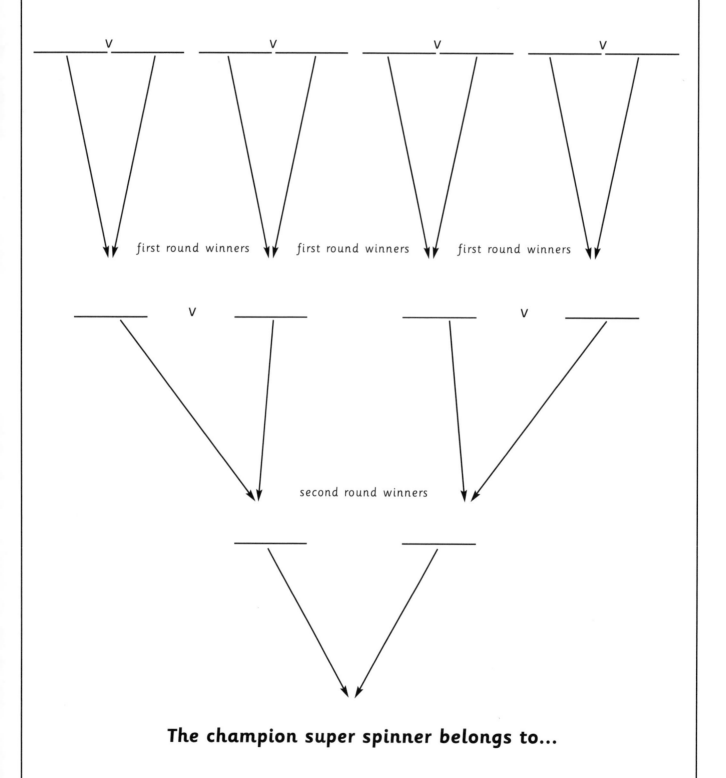

first round winners   first round winners   first round winners

second round winners

The champion super spinner belongs to...

Andrew Brodie Publications © A & C Black Publishers Ltd.

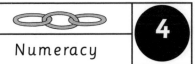
Name: Date:

Super spinner challenge 3

In the box provided draw a diagram of your 'super spinner'. Record the actual measurements and materials used.

If you were making a spinner again, what would you do differently?

_____

_____

_____

Try out your new ideas and have another competition in your group.
Did you make an even better spinner this time?

FRICTION

Name:

Date:

Shape and air resistance

Look at the shapes below.
If each of them was dropped from a height, which do you think would take the longest to reach the ground and why?

I think shape _____ would take longest to reach the ground because

_____

_____

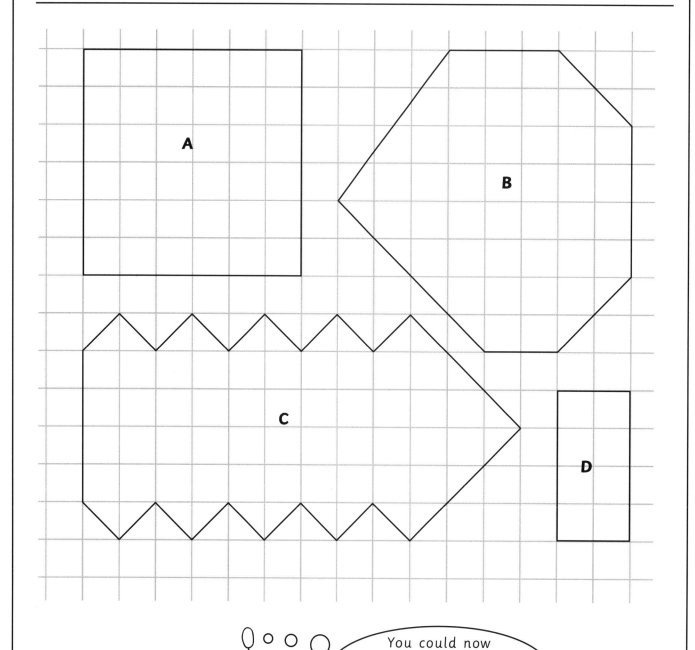

You could now cut out the shapes and test to see if you were right.

 Andrew Brodie Publications © A & C Black Publishers Ltd.

Name:	Date:

Presenting results as a bar chart

Thirty children did a friction test. It involved putting their shoes on a wooden slope to see how steep the slope had to be made before their shoes would slide. Once each pair of shoes had slipped off, they were not put back on again at steeper angles.
Here are the results of the test.

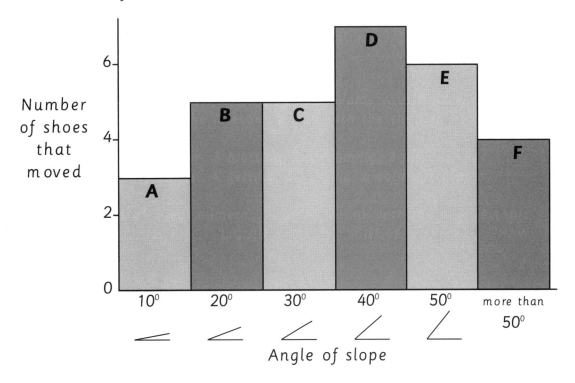

Now answer the questions.

● How many people had shoes that slid down the

slope when it was tipped to 10°? _____

What fraction of the class is that? _____

● How many people had shoes that slid

on the 20° slope? _____

What fraction of the class is that? _____

● Did more or less than half the class have shoes that

needed a slope of <u>more than 30°</u> before they slid? _____

● If you wanted high friction treads on your shoes for icy winter

weather, from which column would you prefer your shoes? _____

Name: Date:

Friction

Plan a fair test to be done in your classroom.

Your test must involve friction. It could be the same as the test about the grip of people's shoes or you might have a better idea of your own.
Describe and illustrate your test here – remember to list the equipment you will need.

Carry out your test. Record the results as a bar chart. Remember to give your chart a title and to label the x and y axes.

Andrew Brodie Publications © A & C Black Publishers Ltd.

Name: Date:

Forces

The pictures below show some PE activities.
Next to each picture write about the forces you can see.
Remember to think about friction and air resistance as well as pushes and pulls.

_____
_____
_____
_____
_____
_____
_____

_____
_____
_____
_____
_____
_____

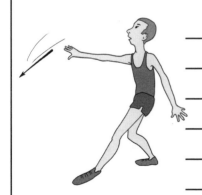

_____
_____
_____
_____
_____
_____

_____
_____
_____
_____
_____

We show possible curriculum links but we will not have thought of everything so you may like to add some of your own.

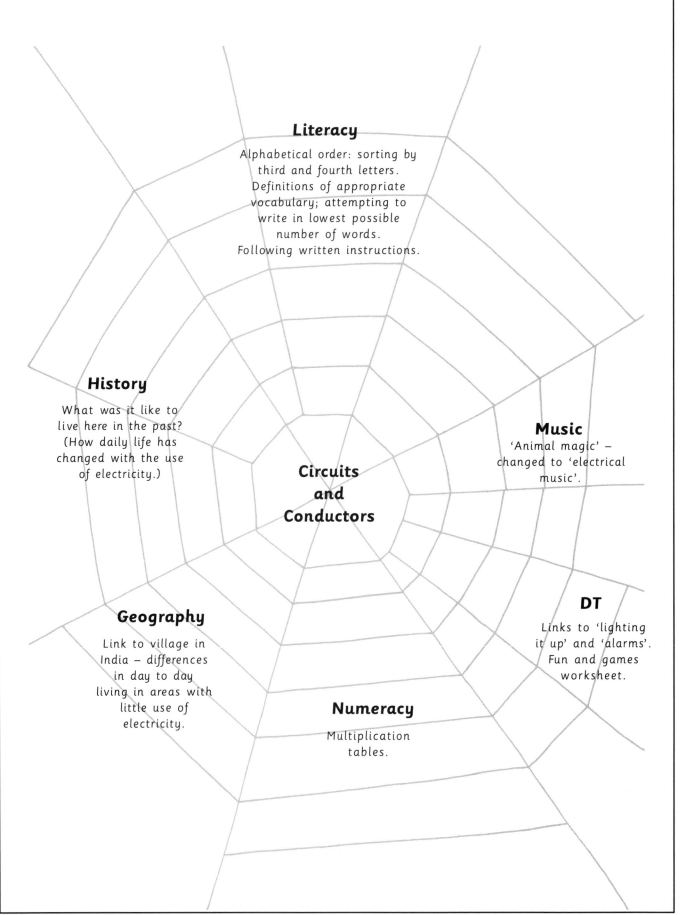

Literacy
Alphabetical order: sorting by third and fourth letters. Definitions of appropriate vocabulary; attempting to write in lowest possible number of words. Following written instructions.

History
What was it like to live here in the past? (How daily life has changed with the use of electricity.)

Music
'Animal magic' – changed to 'electrical music'.

Circuits and Conductors

DT
Links to 'lighting it up' and 'alarms'. Fun and games worksheet.

Geography
Link to village in India – differences in day to day living in areas with little use of electricity.

Numeracy
Multiplication tables.

Andrew Brodie Publications © A & C Black Publishers Ltd.

Worksheet 1 covers word definitions for appropriate vocabulary. The challenge for the children is to write simple definitions using only five words or less.

Worksheet 2 involves categorising words – this sheet provides scope for discussion work as many things are battery operated and recharged from mains electricity. Items such as wristwatches, while now commonly considered to be battery operated, are also available with a winding mechanism. The answers are as follows.

Column A: motor car; personal stereo; hand-held torch; TV remote control; laptop computer; wristwatch.
Column B: washing machine; computer; street light; television; freezer; vacuum cleaner.
Column C: violin; candle; pencil; carpet; biscuit; book.

motor car; laptop; computer; violin; food whisk; street light.

Worksheet 3 concerns alphabetical order, including sorting by third and fourth letters. The answers are as follows.
1 battery; 2 break; 3 bulb; 4 buzzer; 5 cell; 6 circuit; 7 complete; 8 component; 9 conductor; 10 electricity; 11 insulator; 12 mains; 13 metal; 14 motor; 15 plastic; 16 plug; 17 switch; 18 wire.

Worksheet 4 features a wordsearch that requires the children to find the eighteen words from Worksheet 3. The safety message should read: 'Mains electricity is dangerous'.

Worksheets 5 and 6 contain mental maths based on multiplication tables. The answers to the questions on Worksheet 5 are used with the code chart on Worksheet 6 to produce the following message: 'Electricity, in the form of lightning, has been in existence since the beginning of the universe'.

Worksheet 7 covers mental maths based on all tables including using knowledge of tables to find other numbers, for example, 4×16 = double 4×8.
Or $17 \times 7 = (10 \times 7) + (1 \times 7)$.
The three missing answers are: switch; circuit; battery.

Worksheet 8 challenges children to make question boards showing correct facts for use in other subjects. The example given has deliberately not shown children how to construct their circuit as this is the challenge. Each 'fact' board will need to be mounted on card. This task is ideally done as paired work, and can of course use buzzers rather than bulbs. Ensure enough components and materials are available so that boards can be kept in the classroom for use by all children.
Extension – completion of more than one circuit with the board to show several facts, for example capitals of countries within the United Kingdom.

Name: Date:

Defining words

- Look at the words below.
- Working with a partner, discuss what you think each word means.
- Use a dictionary to see if you are right.
- Put the dictionary away!
- Now write your own definition for each word. Try to use five words or less for each definition. The first one has been done for you.

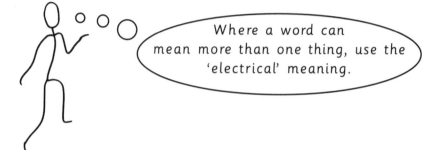

Where a word can mean more than one thing, use the 'electrical' meaning.

circuit   _____ electrical path _____

plug   _____

switch   _____

battery   _____

cell   _____

component   _____

light bulb   _____

electric   _____

conductor   _____

insulator   _____

Andrew Brodie Publications © A & C Black Publishers Ltd.

Name: **Date:**

Sources of power

Look at the words in the battery.
Put them into one of the three sections. You must decide if they **usually** have a battery, are usually mains powered or use **no** electricity.

book   television   computer
street light   candle   pencil
carpet   wristwatch   TV remote control
violin   vacuum cleaner
washing machine   personal stereo
laptop computer   motor car
hand-held torch   biscuit   freezer

Has a battery A	Is mains powered B	Uses no electricity C

Now answer these questions.

🗲 Which of the above items always has a
   battery but has a fuel powered engine?   _____

🗲 Which of the above items usually uses a
   battery that is re-charged from the mains?   _____

🗲 Which item from column C is available
   in an 'electrical' form?   _____

🗲 Which of the following items is available in battery operated, mains powered <u>and</u>
   hand operated versions? Ring the correct answer.

   tumble dryer   food whisk   telephone   flower vase

🗲 What item from column B would
   never be found in a house?   _____

CIRCUITS AND CONDUCTORS

Literacy

Name:

Date:

Alphabetical order

The words below are all connected to your work on electrical circuits.

Take the words from the bulb and arrange them in alphabetical order.

electricity
battery
insulator   mains
plug
cell   component
wire
plastic
conductor
buzzer   motor
switch
complete
break   metal
circuit
bulb

1 _____   2 _____

3 _____   4 _____

5 _____   6 _____

7 _____   8 _____

9 _____ 10 _____ 11 _____ 12 _____

13 _____ 14 _____ 15 _____ 16 _____

17 _____ 18 _____

You will need these words for the next worksheet.

Andrew Brodie Publications © A & C Black Publishers Ltd.

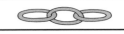

| Name: | Date: |

Wordsearch

1 Find all 18 words from Worksheet 3 in the wordsearch below.
   Shade them carefully. They may be written horizontally →, vertically ↓, or
   diagonally ↘.

i	m	z	m	p	b	a	t	t	e	r	y	b	a	f	h	i	j	k	b
n	c	e	l	l	z	r	w	c	o	n	d	u	c	t	o	r	z	p	u
s	o	n	t	q	w	s	e	w	e	s	w	i	t	c	h	l	m	e	l
u	m	c	x	a	t	q	r	a	i	c	v	z	i	f	t	p	a	x	b
l	p	y	z	h	l	h	i	q	k	b	p	c	i	r	c	u	i	t	f
a	l	w	x	w	z	b	v	b	f	s	b	l	b	v	z	v	n	p	m
t	e	b	u	z	z	e	r	d	h	a	k	n	u	p	j	b	s	h	o
o	t	g	f	b	e	f	k	z	h	k	r	z	h	g	w	x	v	q	t
r	e	p	o	k	c	o	m	p	o	n	e	n	t	h	w	i	x	k	o
z	f	e	l	e	c	t	r	i	c	i	t	y	h	u	v	h	r	b	r
q	z	q	p	v	f	z	p	l	a	s	t	i	c	q	x	w	s	e	q

2 When you have found all the words, shade in the following letters, b, f, h, j, k, p, q, v, w, x and z.

3 Now, reading from left to right and starting at the top, you will find a safety message.

4 Write the safety message on the lines below.

_ _ _ _ _   _ _ _ _ _ _ _ _ _ _   _ _

_ _ _ _ _ _ _ _ _ _.

Name: _____   Date: _____

Electrical multiplication 1

Do you know all your tables? If so, you will do this puzzle easily.

Find the answers to the 16 sets of questions on this sheet. You will need them to help you with the next worksheet. It has been started for you.

1 8 x 8 = _64_
3 x 6 = _18_
8 x 8 = _64_
7 x 4 = _28_
9 x 5 = _45_
9 x 7 = _63_
4 x 9 = _36_
7 x 4 = _28_
6 x 6 = _36_
5 x 9 = _45_
4 x 2 = _8_

2 6 x 6 = ____
7 x 3 = ____

3 5 x 9 = ____
3 x 4 = ____
8 x 8 = ____

4 9 x 6 = ____
12 x 7 = ____
9 x 7 = ____
7 x 7 = ____

5 12 x 7 = ____
6 x 9 = ____

6 6 x 3 = ____
6 x 6 = ____
7 x 8 = ____
2 x 6 = ____
5 x 9 = ____
7 x 3 = ____
4 x 9 = ____
3 x 7 = ____
8 x 7 = ____

7 4 x 3 = ____
5 x 8 = ____
5 x 7 = ____

8 4 x 4 = ____
8 x 8 = ____
8 x 8 = ____
3 x 7 = ____

9 4 x 9 = ____
3 x 7 = ____

10 8 x 8 = ____
10 x 8 = ____
6 x 6 = ____
7 x 5 = ____
5 x 9 = ____
8 x 8 = ____
7 x 3 = ____
7 x 4 = ____
8 x 8 = ____

11 7 x 5 = ____
6 x 6 = ____
3 x 7 = ____
7 x 4 = ____
8 x 8 = ____

12 9 x 5 = ____
6 x 2 = ____
8 x 8 = ____

13 8 x 2 = ____
8 x 8 = ____
8 x 7 = ____
9 x 4 = ____
3 x 7 = ____
7 x 3 = ____
6 x 6 = ____
7 x 3 = ____
7 x 8 = ____

14 12 x 7 = ____
9 x 6 = ____

15 5 x 9 = ____
6 x 2 = ____
8 x 8 = ____

16 4 x 8 = ____
7 x 3 = ____
12 x 3 = ____
6 x 8 = ____
8 x 8 = ____
7 x 9 = ____
5 x 7 = ____
8 x 8 = ____

Andrew Brodie Publications © A & C Black Publishers Ltd.

Name: Date:

Electrical multiplication 2

Each of the 16 sets of questions from Worksheet 5 represents a word from the sentence below. Match each answer to the corresponding letter in this chart. Write the letters in the spaces provided. This will reveal an interesting fact.

a	b	c	d	e	f	g	h	i	j	k	l	m
40	16	28	72	64	54	56	12	36	70	42	18	49

n	o	p	q	r	s	t	u	v	w	x	y	z
21	84	24	60	63	35	45	32	48	27	80	8	9

E l e c t r i c i t y ,   _ _

_ _   _ _ _   _ _

_ _ _ _ _ _ _ _ ,   _ _ _

_ _ _ _   _ _   _ _ _ _ _ _ _ _

_ _ _ _ _   _ _ _

_ _ _ _ _ _ _ _ _   _ _

_ _ _   _ _ _ _ _ _ _ _ .

Name: | Date:

Electrical multiplication 3

Use what you know about multiplication to decode the words. Match each answer to its corresponding letter to do this. The first word has been done for you.

a	b	c	d	e	f	g	h	i	j	k	l	m
135	112	180	62	52	53	48	102	42	99	104	54	150

n	o	p	q	r	s	t	u	v	w	x	y	z
10	4	56	20	128	64	96	60	80	90	32	58	22

4 x 14 = 56
3 x 18 = 54
5 x 12 = 60
2 x 24 = 48

p l u g

---

16 x 4 =
5 x 18 =
3 x 14 =
12 x 8 =
20 x 9 =
6 x 17 =

_ _ _ _ _ _

---

18 x 10 =
2 x 21 =
8 x 16 =
3 x 60 =
20 x 3 =
14 x 3 =
4 x 24 =

_ _ _ _ _ _ _

---

7 x 16 =
27 x 5 =
6 x 16 =
3 x 32 =
4 x 13 =
32 x 4 =
29 x 2 =

_ _ _ _ _ _ _

Now make a coded word for a friend to work out.

Andrew Brodie Publications © A & C Black Publishers Ltd.

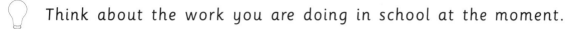
Name: | Date:

Fun and games

💡 Think about the work you are doing in school at the moment.

💡 You are going to use what you know about circuits to help you to remember facts you have learned in other subjects.

💡 Look at the example below. When the circuit is completed correctly, the bulb will light up.

metal paper fasteners

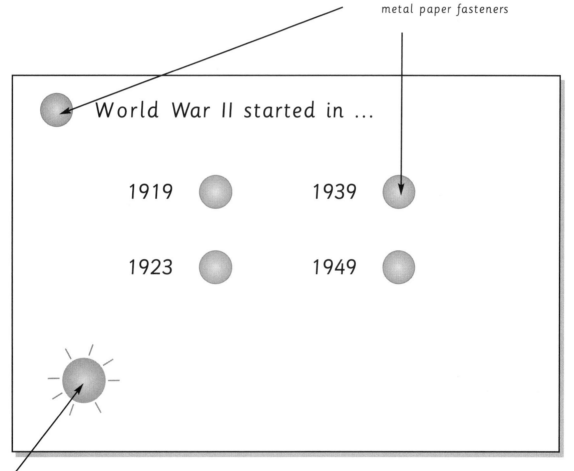

World War II started in ...

1919   1939

1923   1949

light bulb

💡 That is just one idea – have a look at the card and electrical components your teacher has put out for use – Your ideas could be much better.

CIRCUITS AND CONDUCTORS

Music

Name: Date:

Electrical music

✔ In a small group, think about what musical sounds are used to imitate other things, for example the tapping together of coconut shells can remind us of the sound of horses' hooves.
Now think about some electrical items and their sounds.

✔ **Challenge**
Choose four electrical items. Use musical instruments to make sounds that remind you of the noises they make.
Record what you do in the boxes below. Write down which instruments you use and the pitch, note length, rhythm, etc.

Object 1 _____

Object 2 _____

Object 3 _____

Object 4 _____

✔ Play the best of your 'music' to the class. What object do they think your sound represents?

Andrew Brodie Publications © A & C Black Publishers Ltd.